Community Song Book

Alphabetical Index

This Edition © 1996 International Music Publications Limited
Southend Road, Woodford Green, Essex IG8 8HN, England
Reproducing this music in any form is illegal and forbidden by the Copyright, Designs and Patents Act 1988.

1

The Bailiff's Daughter Of Islington

Traditional

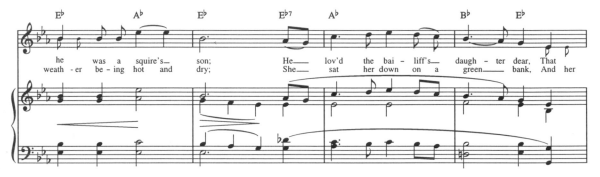

3.
"Before I give you a penny, sweetheart,
Pray tell me where you were born;"
"At Islington, kind sir," she said,
"Where I have had many a scorn"
"I prythee, sweetheart, tell to me,
O tell me if you know
The bailiff's daughter of Islington?"
"She is dead, sir, long ago."

4.
"If she be dead, then take my horse,
My saddle and bridle also,
For I will to some far country,
Where no man shall me know."
"Oh stay, oh stay, thou goodly youth,
She standeth by thy side!
She is here, alive, she is not dead,
And ready to be thy bride."

Barbara Allen

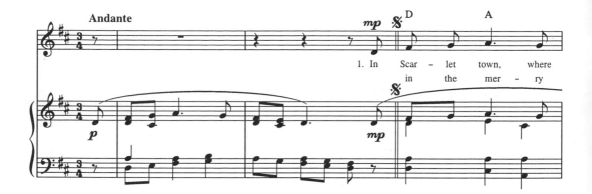

1. In Scar - let town, where
in the mer - ry

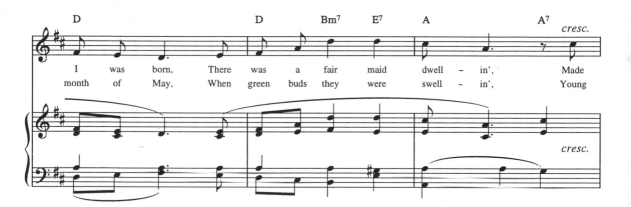

I was born, There was a fair maid dwell - in', Made
month of May, When green buds they were swell - in', Young

ev - 'ry youth cry, "Well - a - day!" Her name was Bar - b'ra Al - len. 2. All
Jem - my Grove on his death - bed lay For love of Bar - b'ra Al - len.

3
So slowly, slowly she came up,
And slowly she came nigh him,
And all she said when there she came,
"Young man, I think you're dying!"

4
When he was dead and laid in grave,
Her heart was struck with sorrow;
"O mother dear! Come make my bed,
For I shall die tomorrow."

Come, Lasses And Lads

Traditional

4

5. Now there they did stay the whole of the day,
And tired the fiddler quite,
With dancing and play, without any pay,
From morning unto night.
They told the fiddler then
They'd pay him for his play;
And each a twopence, twopence, twopence,
Gave him, and went away.

6. "Good-night", says Harry, "Good-night", says Mary,
"Good-night", says Dolly to John;
"Good-night", says Sue, "Good-night", says Hugh,
"Good-night", says every one.
Some walked, and some did run,
Some loitered on the way;
And bound themselves by kisses twelve
To meet the next holiday.

Drink To Me Only With Thine Eyes

BEN JOHNSON

Old English Air

1. Drink to me on- ly with thine eyes,— And
2. I sent thee late a ro- sy wreath Not

I— will pledge with mine,— Or leave a kiss with- in— the cup,— And I'll— not ask for
so— much hon- 'ring thee,— As giv- ing it a hope— that there— It could not with- er'd

wine;— The thirst that from the soul— doth rise Doth ask a drink di- vine,—
be;— But thou— there- on didst on- ly breathe, And sent'st it back to me,—

But might I of Love's nec— tar sip,— I would not change for thine.
Since when it grows, and smells, I swear,— Not of— it- self but thee.

Early One Morning

1. Ear - ly one morn - ing, just as the sun was ris - ing, I heard a maid
2. gay is the gar - land, and fresh are the ro - ses I've cull'd from the

sing in the val - ley be - low; "Oh! don't de - ceive me, Oh! nev - er
gar - den to bind on thy brow; "Oh! don't de - ceive me, Oh! nev - er

leave me, How could you use a poor maid - en so?" 2. Oh!

3. Remember the vows that you made to your Mary,
Remember the bow'r where you vow'd to be true;
"Oh! don't deceive me *etc.*"

4. Thus sang the poor maiden, her sorrow bewailing,
Thus sang the poor maid in the valley below -
"Oh! don't deceive me *etc.*"

The Farmer's Boy

Old English Song

4.

The farmer's wife cried, "Try the lad,
Let him no longer seek;"
"Yes, father, do." the daughter cried,
While the tears rolled down her cheek.
"For those who would work it's hard to want,
And wander for employ.
Don't let him go, but let him stay
And be a farmer's boy."

5.

The farmer's boy grew up a man,
And the good old couple died;
They left the lad the farm they had,
And the daughter for his bride.
Now the lad that was, and the farm now has,
Often thinks and smiles with joy,
And blesses the day he came that way
To be a farmer's boy.

The Fine Old English Gentleman

1. I'll sing you a good old song, That was made by a good old pate, Of a
Hall so old, was hung a-bout With pikes and guns and bows, And

fine old Eng-lish Gen-tle-man Who had an old es-tate; And who kept up his old man-sion At a
sword and good old buck-lers Which had stood against old foes; 'Twas there "His Wor-ship" sat in state In

boun-ti-ful old rate, With a good old por-ter to re-lieve The old poor at his gate, Like a
doub-let and trunk hose, And quaff'd his cup of good old sack, To warm his good old nose,

fine old Eng-lish Gen-tle-man, One of the old-en time 2. His

3. His custom was, when Christmas came,
To bid his friends repair
To his old hall, where feast and ball
For them he did prepare;
And tho' the rich he entertained,
He ne'er forgot the poor;
Nor were there any destitute
E'er driven from the door
Of this good old English Gentleman,
One of the olden time.

4. But time, though sweet, is strong in flight,
And years roll swiftly by;
And Autumn's falling leaves proclaim'd
This good old man must die.
He laid him down right tranquilly
Gave up life's latest sigh,
A mournful silence reign'd around,
And tears bedewed each eye
For this fine old English Gentleman,
One of the olden time.

Gather Ye Rose-buds While You May

ROBERT HERRICK
(1591 - 1674)

WILLIAM LAWES
(1590 - 1645)

1. Gath - er ye rose - buds while ye may, Old time is still a - fly - ing; And
2. glo - ri - ous lamp of heaven, the Sun, The high - er he's a - get - ting, The

this same flower that smiles to - day, To - mor - row will be dy - ing. 2. The
soon - er will his race be run, And near - er he's to set - ting.

3. That age is best, which is the first,
When youth and blood are warmer;
But being spent, the worst and worst
Times still succeed the former.

4. Then be not coy, but use your time,
And while ye may, go marry;
For having lost but once your prime,
You may for ever tarry.

God Save The Queen

1. God save our gra - cious Queen, Long live our no - ble Queen,
2. O Lord our God a - rise, Scat - ter her en - e - mies,

God save the Queen. Send her, vic - tor - i - ous, Hap - py and
And make them fall! Con - found their pol - i - tics, Frus - trate their

glo - ri - ous, Long to reign o - ver us, God save the Queen.
knav - ish tricks, On Thee our hopes we fix, God save us all.

3   Thy choicest gifts in store,
    On her be pleased to pour,
    Long may she reign.
    May she defend our laws,
    And ever give us cause
    To sing with heart and voice,
    God save the Queen!

Golden Slumbers

A 17th Century Lullaby

Andante

1. Gol – den slum – bers kiss your eyes, Smiles a – wake you when you rise, Sleep pret – ty dar – ling, do not cry,— And I will sing a lul – la – by, lul – la – by, lul – la – by, lul – – – la – by.

2. Care you know not, there – fore sleep, While I o'er you watch do keep. Sleep pret – ty dar – ling, do not

Here's A Health Unto His Majesty

By JEREMY SAVILE

12

It Was A Lover And His Lass

"SHAKESPEARE"

T. MORLEY (1600)

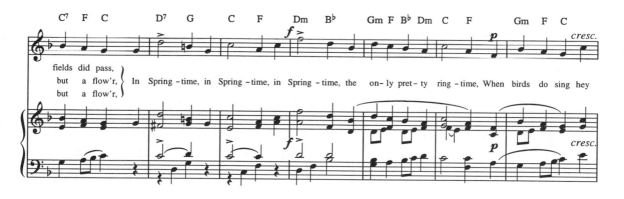

The Lass Of Richmond Hill

J. HOOK

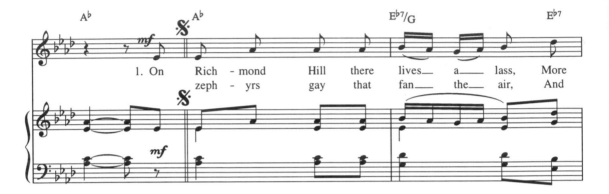

1. On Rich - mond Hill there lives__ a__ lass, More
   zeph - yrs gay that fan__ the__ air, And

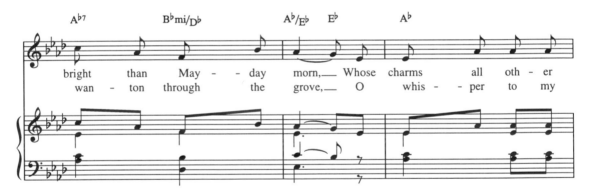

bright than May - -day morn,__ Whose charms all oth - er
wan - ton through the grove,__ O whis - -per to my

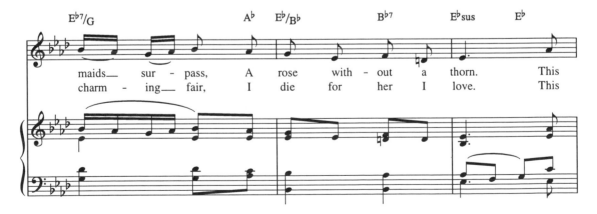

maids__ sur - pass, A rose with - out a thorn. This
charm - ing__ fair, I die for her I love. This

The Lincolnshire Poacher

Old English

4. I threw him on my shoulder, and then we trudgéd home,
We took him to a neighbour's house and sold him for a crown,
We sold him for a crown, my boys, but I need not tell you where.
Oh, tis my delight *etc.*

5. Success to every gentleman that lives in Lincolnshire,
Success to every poacher that wants to sell a hare,
Bad luck to every gamekeeper that will not sell his deer.
Oh, tis my delight *etc.*

The Miller Of The Dee

A 17th Century Song

Oh! Dear! What Can The Matter Be?

Old English Song

Oh! The Oak And The Ash

17th Century

Rule Britannia

Dr. ARNE

Sally In Our Alley

HENRY CAREY

1. Of all the girls that are so smart, There's none like pret-ty Sal-ly, She is the dar-ling of my heart, And lives in our al-ley. There is no la-dy in the land That's half so sweet as Sal-ly, She is the dar-ling of my heart, And lives in our al-ley. 2. Of all the

days with-in the week, I dear-ly love but one day, And that's the day that comes be-twixt, A Sat-ur-day and Mon-day. For then I'm dress'd all in my best, To walk a-broad with Sal-ly, She is the dar-ling of my heart, And lives in our al-ley. 3. My mas-ter

and the neigh-bours all Make game of me and Sal-ly; And but for her I'd ra-ther be A slave, and row a gal-ley. But when my se-ven long years are out, Oh, then I'll mar-ry Sal-ly; And then how hap-pi-ly we'll live! But not in our al-ley.

Moderato

Fine

Since First I Saw Your Face

THOMAS FORD (1580 - 1648)

1. Since first I saw your face, I re-solv'd To
hon - our and re - nown you; If now I be dis - dained, I wish My
heart had nev - er known you, What! I that lov'd, and you that liked, Shall we be - gin to
wran - gle? No, no, no, my heart is fast, And can - not dis - en - tan - gle 2. The

Sun, whose beams most glor - i - ous are, Re-
jec - teth no be - hold - er; And your sweet beau - ty, past com - pare, Made
my poor eyes the bold - er. When beau - ty moves, and wit de - lights, And sighs of kind - ness
bind me, There, O there, where' - er I go, I'll leave my heart be - hind me.

Sweet And Low
A LULLABY

"TENNYSON"

J. BARNBY

1. Sweet and low, sweet and low, Wind of the west - ern sea; Low, low, breathe and blow, Wind of the west - ern sea, O - ver the roll - ing wa - ters go, Come from the dy - ing moon and blow, blow him a - gain to me, While my lit - tle one, while my pret - ty one sleeps.

2. Sleep and rest, sleep and rest, Fa - ther will come to thee soon; Rest, rest on mo - ther's breast, Fa - ther will come to thee soon, Fa - ther will come to his babe in the nest, Sil - ver sails all out of the West, Un - der the sil - ver moon, Sleep, my lit - tle one, sleep, my pret - ty one, sleep.

The Vicar Of Bray

17th Century

Allegretto

1. In good King Char - les' gold - en days, When loy - al - ty no harm meant, A zea - lous High Church - man was I, And so I got pre - fer - ment; To teach my flock I nev - er miss'd, Kings were by God ap -

roy - al James ob - tain'd the crown, And Pop - 'ry came in fash - ion, The pe - nal laws I hoot - ed down, And read the De - clar - a - tion; The Church of Rome I found would fit Full well my con - sti -

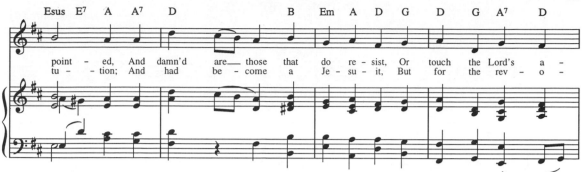

3. When William was our king declared,
To ease a nation's grievance,
With this new wind about I steer'd
And swore to him allegiance;
Old principles I did revoke,
Set conscience at a distance;
Passive obediance was a joke,
A jest was non-resistance.
And this is law, *etc.*

4. When gracious Anne became our Queen,
The Church of England's glory,
Another face of things was seen,
And I became a Tory;
Occasional Conformists base,
I damn'd their moderation,
And thought the church in danger was,
By such prevarication.
And this is law, *etc.*

5. When George in pudding-time came o'er,
And moderate men look'd big, sir,
I turned a cat-in-a-pan once more,
And so became a whig, sir;
And thus, preferment I procured,
From our new faith's defender,
And almost every day abjured
The Pope and the Pretender.
And this is law, *etc.*

6. The Illustrious house of Hanover
And Protestant succession,
To these I do allegiance swear,
While they can keep possession;
For in my faith and loyalty
I never more will falter,
And George my lawful King shall be,
Until the times do alter.
And this is law, *etc.*

Uncle Tom Cobleigh
(WIDDICOMBE FAIR)

Old Devonshire Song

3. Then Friday came, and Saturday noon,
All along, down along, out along lee;
But Tom Pearse's old mare have not trotted home,
With Bill Brewer &c.   *Chorus*

4. So Tom Pearse he got up to the top o' the hill,
All along, down along, out along lee;
And he seed his old mare down a making her will,
With Bill Brewer &c.   *Chorus*

5. So Tom Pearse's old mare her took sick and died,
All along, down along, out along lee;
And Tom he sat down on a stone, and he cried
With Bill Brewer &c.   *Chorus*

6. But this isn't the end o' this shocking affair,
All along, down along, out along lee;
Nor, though they be dead, of the horrid career
Of Bill Brewer &c.   *Chorus*

7. When the wind whistles cold on the moor of a night,
All along, down along, out along lee;
Tom Pearse's old mare doth appear, gashly white,
With Bill Brewer &c.   *Chorus*

8. And all the long night be heard skirling and groans,
All along, down along, out along lee;
From Tom Pearse's old mare in her rattling bones,
And Bill Brewer &c.   *Chorus*

Annie Laurie

Auld Lang Syne

ROBERT BURNS

Scotch Song

Green Grow The Rashes, O!

BURNS

Air about 1700

3. And you sae douce, wha sneer at this,
Ye're nought but senseless asses, O!
The wisest man the warld e'er saw,
He dearly lo'ed the lasses, O!
Green grow the rashes, O!   etc.

4. Auld Nature swears, the lovely dears
Her noblest works she classes, O!
Her 'prentice han' she tried on man,
An' then she made the lasses, O!
Green grow the rashes, O!   etc.

The Blue Bell Of Scotland

Words by MRS GRANT

3

Oh! what, tell me what if your Highland lad be slain?
Oh! what, tell me what if your Highland lad be slain?
Oh, no! true love will be his guard and bring him safe again,
For it's oh! my heart would break if my Highland lad were slain.
Oh, no! true love will be his guard,   *etc.*

Loch Lomond

Scots, Wha Hae Wi' Wallace Bled

Words by
BURNS

Ye Banks And Braes

ROBERT BURNS

1. Ye banks and braes o' Bon - nie Doon, How can ye bloom sae
have I roved by Bon - nie Doon, To see the rose and

fresh and fair! How can ye chant, ye, lit - tle birds, And I sae wea - ry,
wood - bine twine; And il - ka bird sang o' its love, And fond - ly sae did

fu' o' care! Thou'lt break my heart, thou warb - ling bird, That wan - tons thro' the
I o' mine. Wi' light - some heart, I pu'd a rose, Fu' sweet up - on its

flow' - ring thorn; Thou mindst me of de - part - ed joys, De - part - ed, nev - er to re - turn 2. Oft
thorn - y tree; And my fause lov - er stole my rose, But ah! he left the thorn wi' me.

Cockles And Mussels

Irish Song

Come Back To Erin

By CLARIBEL

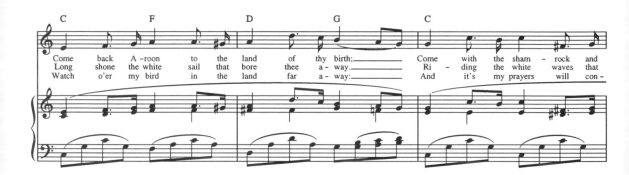

1. Come back to E - rin, Ma - vour - neen, Ma - vour - neen!
2. O - ver the green sea, Ma - vour - neen, Ma - vour - neen,
3. O may the An - gels, a - wak - in' and sleep - in'

Come back A - roon to the land of thy birth;_____ Come with the sham - rock and
Long shone the white sail that bore thee a - way._____ Ri - ding the white waves that
Watch o'er my bird in the land far a - way:_____ And it's my prayers will con -

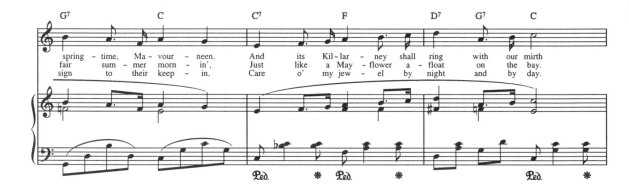

spring - time, Ma - vour - neen, And its Kil - lar - ney shall ring with our mirth
fair sum - mer morn - in', Just like a May - flower a - float on the bay.
sign to their keep - in, Care o' my jew - el by night and by day.

The Harp That Once

THOMAS MOORE

Irish Melody

Killarney

Words by E. FALCONER

Music by BALFE

1. By Kil-lar-ney's lakes and fells, Em'-rald isles and winding bays. Moun-tain paths and wood-land dells, Mem'-'ry ev-er fond-ly strays. Boun-teous na-ture loves all lands, Beau-ty wan-ders ev-'ry-where. Foot-prints leaves on ma-ny strands,— But her home is sure-ly there! An-gels fold their wings and rest In that E-den of the West; Beau-ty's home, Kil-lar-ney, Heav'ns re-flex,— Kil-lar-ney.

2. No place else can charm the eye, With such bright and var-ied tints. Ev-'ry rock that you pass by, Ver-dure broi-ders or be-sprints Vir-gin there the green grass grows, Ev-'ry morn Spring's na-tal day; Bright hued ber-ries daff the snows,— Smil-ing Win-ter's frown a-way. An-gels, of-ten paus-ing there, Doubt if E-den were more fair; Beau-ty's home, Kil-lar-ney, Heav'ns re-flex,— Kil-lar-ney.

The Last Rose Of Summer

Words by THOMAS MOORE

The Minstrel Boy

MOORE *(Irish Melodies)*

1.The Min -strel boy___ to the war is gone, In the
ranks of death___ you'll find him; His fa -ther's sword he has gird - ed on, And his
wild harp slung___ be -hind him, "Land of Song" said the war-rior bard, "Tho' all the world be -
trays thee, One sword at least thy___ rights shall guard, One___ faith - ful heart___ shall praise thee!" 2.The

Min -strel fell,___ but the foe -man's chain Could not
bring his proud___ soul un -- der; The harp he loved___ ne'er___ spoke a -gain For he
tore its chords___ a -sun -- der, And said; "No chain shall___ sul -ly thee, Thou soul of love and
brav - er- y! Thy songs were made for the pure and free, They ne'er shall sound___ in sla -'ry!"

All Through The Night

Words by T.OLIPHANT

Welsh Tune

1.While the moon her watch is keep - ing, All through the night;
2.Fond - ly, then, I dream of thee, love, All through the night;

While the wea - ry world is sleep - ing, All through the night;
Wak - ing, still thy form I see, love, All through the night;

O'er my bo - som gent - ly steal - ing, Vis - ions of de - light re - veal - ing,
When this mor - tal coil is o - ver, Will thy gen - tle spi - rit ho - ver

Breathes a pure and ho - ly feel - ing, All through the night.
O'er the bed where sleeps thy lov - er All through the night.

God Bless The Prince Of Wales

Words by GEORGE LINLEY

Music by BRINLEY RICHARDS

Men Of Harlech

Words by EDWARD LOCKTON

Welsh Melody

With your trum – pets sound – ing, Wild – ly forth be bound – ing,
Spear on spear is crash – ing Man on man is dash – ing,

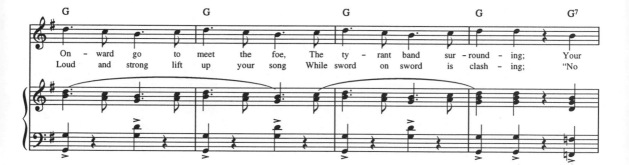

On – ward go to meet the foe, The ty – rant band sur – round – ing; Your
Loud and strong lift up your song While sword on sword is clash – ing; "No

an – cient ban – ners wav – ing o'er ye, Rank on — rank fall back be – fore ye,
fet – ter shall be ours, no hal – ter, Ne'er a — foe our laws shall al – ter,

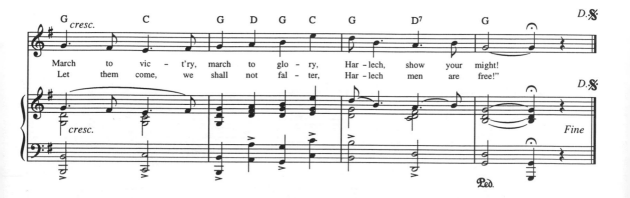

March to vic – t'ry, march to glo – ry, Har – lech, show your might!
Let them come, we shall not fal – ter, Har – lech men are free!"

A-Roving

Sea Shanty

The Bay Of Biscay

ANDREW CHERRY

J. DAVY

1. Loud roar'd the dread-ful thun-der, The rain, a del-uge show'rs, The
2. Now dash'd up-on the bil-low, Her op-'ning tim-bers creak, Each

clouds were rent a-sun-der By light-ning's vi-vid powers. The night was drear and dark, Our
fears a wa-t'ry pil-low None stop the dred-ful leak. To cling to slip-p'ry shrouds, Each

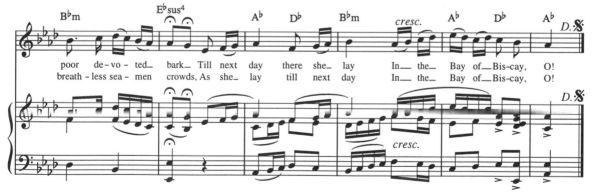

poor de-vo-ted bark Till next day there she lay In the Bay of Bis-cay, O!
breath-less sea-men crowds, As she lay till next day In the Bay of Bis-cay, O!

3. At length the wish'd for morrow
   Broke thro' the hazy sky,
   Absorb'd in silent sorrow
   Each heav'd a bitter sigh.
   The dismal wreck to view
   Struck horror on that crew,
   As she lay all that day
   In the Bay of Biscay, O!

4. Her yielding timbers sever,
   Her pitchy seams are rent,
   When heaven all bounteous ever,
   Its boundless mercy sent,
   A sail in sight appears,
   We hail her three cheers;
   Now we sail, with the gale,
   From the Bay of Biscay, O!

Blow The Man Down!

Sea Shanty

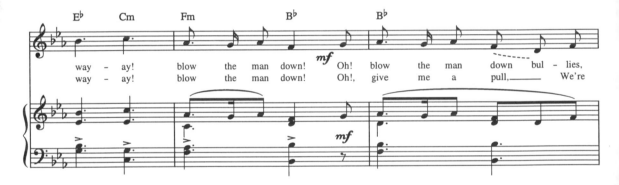

3. Oh! blow the man down, bullies, blow the man down!
   Oh! way-ay! blow the man down!
   Oh! give her a pull and we'll send her along,
   Oh! gimme some time to blow the man down.

4. As I was a-walking down Rotherhithe street,
   Oh! way-ay! blow the man down!
   A pretty young creature, I chanced for to meet,
   Oh! gimme some time to blow the man down.

The British Grenadiers

Haul On The Bowlin'

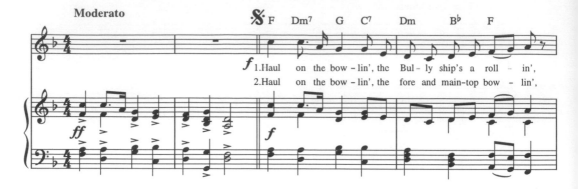

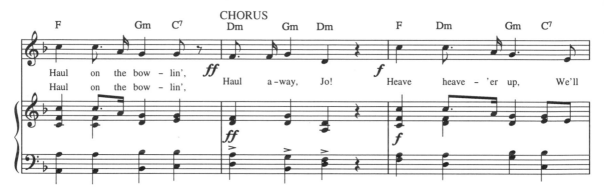

3. Haul on the bowlin', the packet is a rollin',
   Haul on the bowlin', Haul away Jo!
   Heave, heave'er up, *etc..*

4. Haul on the bowlin', the skipper he's a-growlin',
   Haul on the bowlin', haul away Jo!
   Heave, heave'er up, *etc..*

5. Haul on the bowlin', to London we are goin',
   Haul on the bowlin', Haul away Jo!
   Heave, heave'er up, *etc..*

6. Haul on the bowlin', the main-topgallant howlin',
   Haul on the bowlin', haul away Jo!
   Heave, heave'er up, *etc..*

Heart Of Oak

DAVID GARRICK 1750

WILLIAM BOYCE

3. Still Britain shall triumph, her ships plough the sea,
Her standard be Justice, her watchword 'Be free';
Then cheer up, my lads, with one heart let us sing,
Our soldiers, our sailors, our statesmen, our King.
Heart of Oak etc..

The Mermaid

Traditional

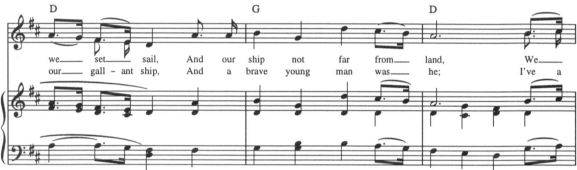

rag - ing seas___ did___ roar,_____ And the storm - y winds did___ blow, While

we jol - ly sail - or boys were sit - ting up a - loft, And the land lub - bers ly - ing down be -

low, be - low, be - low, And the land lub - bers ly - ing down be - low. 2.Then___

Fine

3. Then up starts the mate of our gallant ship,
   And a bold yound man was he;
   Oh! I have a wife in fair Portsmouth town,
   But a widow I fear she will be, & c.
   For the raging seas, & c.

4. Then up starts the cook of our gallant ship,
   And a gruff old soul was he;
   Oh! I have a wife in fair Plymouth town,
   But a widow I fear she will be, & c.
   For the raging seas, & c.

5. Then up spoke the little cabin-boy,
   And a pretty little boy was he;
   Oh! I am griev'd for my daddy and my mammy,
   Than you for wives all three, & c.
   For the raging seas, & c.

6. Then three times round went our gallant ship,
   And three times round went she;
   For the want of a life-boat they all went down,,
   And she sank to the bottom of the sea, & c.
   For the raging seas, & c.

Pack Up Your Troubles (In Your Old Kit Bag)

Words by GEORGE ASAF

Music by FELIX POWELL

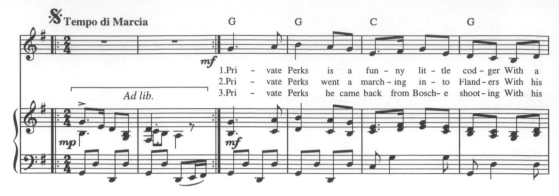

1. Pri – vate Perks is a fun – ny lit – tle cod – ger With a
2. Pri – vate Perks went a march – ing in – to Fland – ers With his
3. Pri – vate Perks he came back from Bosch – e shoot – ing With his

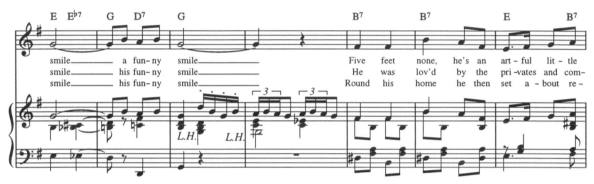

smile_____ a fun – ny smile_____ Five feet none, he's an art – ful lit – tle
smile_____ his fun – ny smile_____ He was lov'd by the pri – vates and com –
smile_____ his fun – ny smile_____ Round his home he then set a – bout re –

dod – ger With a smile_____ a sun – ny smile_____ Flush or broke, he'll
man – ders For his smile_____ his sun – ny smile_____ When a throng of
cruit – ing With his smile_____ his sun – ny smile_____ He told all his

have his lit – tle joke, He can't be sup – press'd_____ All the
Ger – mans came a – long, With a might – y swing,_____ Perks yell'd
pals, the short, the tall, What a time he'd had;_____ And as

Rio Grande

Shenandoah

Sea Shanty

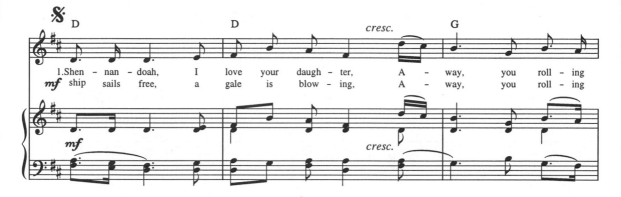

1. Shen - nan - doah, I love your daugh - ter, A - way, you roll - ing
ship sails free, a gale is blow - ing, A - way, you roll - ing

ri - ver!___ Shen - an - doah, I long to hear you; A -
ri - ver!___ The bra - ces taut, the sheets a - flow - ing, A -

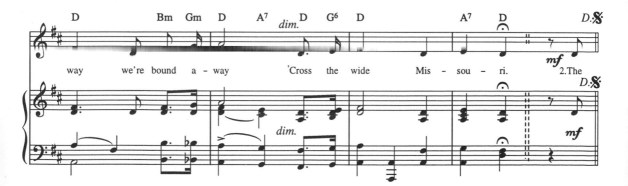

way we're bound a - way 'Cross the wide Mis - sou - ri. 2.The

3. Shenandoah, I'll ne'er forget you,
   Away you rolling river!
   Till I die, I'll love you ever,
   Away, we're bound away
   'Cross the wide Missouri.

The Soldiers' Chorus (Faust)

CHARLES GOUNOD

Glo – ry and love to the men of old!

Their sons may co–py their vir–tues bold, Cou – rage in heart and a sword in hand,

Rea–dy to fight, or rea–dy to die for Fa – ther–land! Who needs bid–ding to dare,

by a trum–pet blown? Who lacks pi–ty to spare when the field is won?

Who would fly from a foe____ if a-lone or last?____ And boast he was true, as co-ward might do, when

per - il is past?____ Glo - ry and love to the men of old!____ Their sons may

co-py their vir-tues bold,____ Cou - rage in heart and a sword in hand,____ Ready to fight for Fa - ther-

land, or ready to die,____ for Fa - ther-land, or ready to die,_____ or ready to

die,_____ for Fa - ther - land.

What Shall We Do With A Drunken Sailor?

Sea Shanty

Come, Landlord, Fill The Flowing Bowl

Old English

4. But he who drinks just what he likes,
   And getteth half seas over,
   Will live until he die perhaps,
   And then lie down in clover.

5. But he who kisses a pretty girl,
   And goes and tells his mother,
   Ought to have his lips cut off,
   And never kiss another.

A-Hunting We Will Go

Words by HENRY FIELDING

Traditional

1. The dus - ky night rides down the sky, And ush - ers in the morn; The hounds all join in glor - i - ous cry, The hounds all join in glor - i - ous cry, The

wife a - round her hus - - band throws Her arms, and begs him stay; "My dear, it rains, it hails, it snows, My dear, it rains, it hails, it snows, You

brush - ing fox in yon - - der wood, Se - cure to find we seek; For why, I car - ried, sound and good, For why, I car - ried, sound and good, A

4. Away he goes, he flies the rout,
   Their steeds they soundly switch;
   Some are thrown in, and some thrown out,
   And some thrown in the ditch.
   But a-hunting we will go.

5. At length his strength to faintness worn,
   Poor Reynard ceases flight;
   Then hungry, homeward we return,
   To feast away the night.
   Then a-drinking we do go.

Down Among The Dead Men

"DYER"

About 1700

3. In smiling Bacchus' joys I'll roll,
Deny no pleasure to my soul,
Let Bacchus' health now briskly move,
For Bacchus is a friend of love.
And he that will this health deny,
Down among the dead men let him lie!

4. May love and wine their rights maintain,
And their united pleasures reign,
While Bacchus' treasure crown the board,
We'll sing the joys that both afford;
And they that won't with us comply,
Down among the dead men let them lie!

For He's A Jolly Good Fellow

For he's a jol-ly good fel-low, For he's a jol-ly good

fel - low, For he's a jol-ly good fel - - low, And so say all of

us,_____ And so say all of us,_____ And so say all of us,_____ For

he's a jol-ly good fel - low, For he's a jol-ly good fel - low, For

he's a jol-ly good fel - - low, And so say all of us._____

Here's To The Maiden Of Bashful Fifteen

Words by SHERIDAN

Music by THOMAS LINLEY

John Peel

Moderato

1. Do ye ken John Peel with his coat so grey, Do ye
ken John Peel and Ru-by too,
here's to John Peel from my heart and soul, Let's

ken John Peel at the break of the day, Do ye ken John Peel when he's far, far a-way, With his
Ran-ter and Ring-wood, Bell-man and True, From a find to a check, from a check to a view, From a
drink to his health, let's fin-ish the bowl, We'll fol-low John Peel through fair and thro' foul, If we

CHORUS

hounds and his horn in the morn - ing?
view to a death in the morn - ing. For the sound of his horn brought me from my bed, And the cry of his hounds which he
want a good hunt in the morn - ing.

oft-times led; Peel's tal-ly ho would a-wak-en the dead, Or the fox from his lair in the morn-ing. *D.S.*
3. Then

Fine

4. Do ye ken John Peel with his coat so grey?
He lived at Troutbeck once on a day;
Now he has gone far, far, far away,
We shall ne'er hear his voice in the morning.
For the sound of his horn. *etc.*

There Is A Tavern In The Town

Adapted from
A Cornish Folk-Song

The Little Brown Jug

By R. A. EASTBURN

3. When I go toiling to my farm,
   I take little "Brown Jug" under my arm;
   I place it under a shady tree,
   Little "Brown Jug" 'tis you and me. *Chorus*

4. If all the folks in Adam's race,
   Were gathered together in one place;
   Then I'd prepare to shed a tear,
   Before I'd part from you, my dear. *Chorus*

5. If I'd a cow that gave such milk,
   I'd clothe her in the finest silk;
   I'd feed her on the choicest hay,
   And milk her forty times a day. *Chorus*

4. The rose is red, my nose is, too,
   The violet's blue, and so are you;
   And yet I guess before I stop,
   We'd better take another drop. *Chorus*

The Animals Went In Two By Two

American Tune

3. The animals went in four by four,
   The great hippopotamus stuck in the door.

4. The animals went in five by five,
   By eating each other they kept alive.

5. The animals went in six by six,
   They turned out the monkey because of his tricks.

6. The animals went in seven by seven,
   The little pig thought he was going to heaven.

Camptown Races

S. C. FOSTER

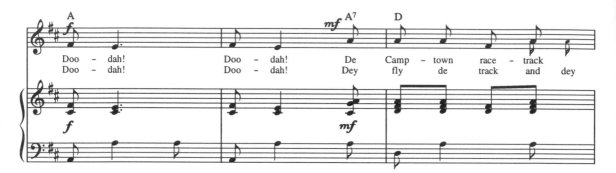

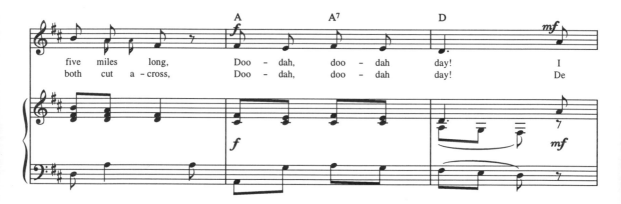

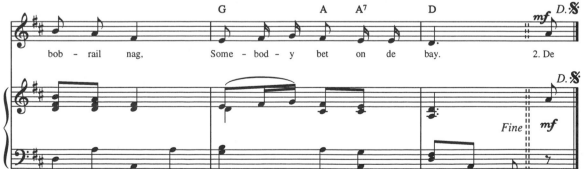

3. Old muley cow came on de track — Doodah, *etc.*
De bob-tail fling her ober his back, — Doodah-day!
Den fly along like a railroad car — Doodah, *etc.*
Runnin' a race wid a shootin' star — Doodah-day!
Gwine to run all night! *etc.*

4. See dem flyin' on a ten-mile heat — Doodah, *etc.*
Round de race-track, den repeat — Doodah-day!
I win my money on de bob-tail nag — Doodah, *etc.*
I keep my money in an old tow bag — Doodah-day!
Gwine to run all night! *etc.*

Marching Through Georgia

By HENRY C. WORK

In March time

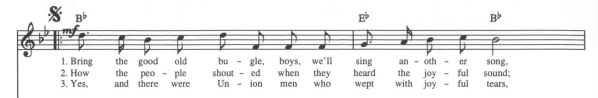

1. Bring the good old bu – gle, boys, we'll sing an – oth – er song,
2. How the peo – ple shout – ed when they heard the joy – ful sound;
3. Yes, and there were Un – ion men who wept with joy – ful tears,

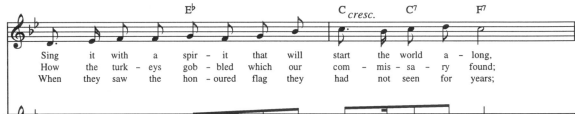

Sing it with a spir – it that will start the world a – long,
How the turk – eys gob – bled which our com – mis – sa – ry found;
When they saw the hon – oured flag they had not seen for years;

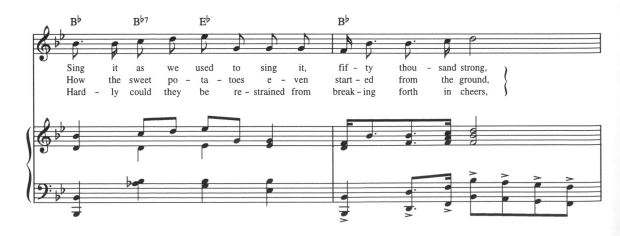

Sing it as we used to sing it, fif – ty thou – sand strong,
How the sweet po – ta – toes e – ven start – ed from the ground,
Hard – ly could they be re – strained from break – ing forth in cheers,

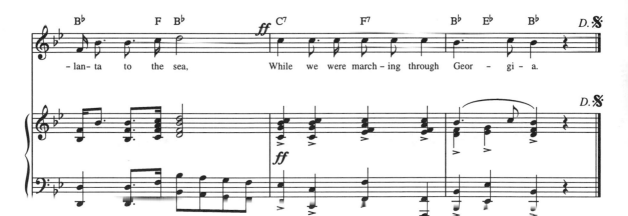

4. "Sherman's dashing Yankee boys will never reach the coast,"
   So the saucy rebels said, and 'twas no idle boast;
   Had they not forgot, alas, to reckon with the host,
   While we were marching through Georgia.
   Hurrah! hurrah! *etc.*

5. So we made a thoroughfare for Freedom and her train,
   Sixty miles in latitude, three hundred to the main;
   Treason fled before us, for resistance was in vain,
   While we were marching through Georgia.
   Hurrah! hurrah! *etc.*

My Old Kentucky Home

S. C. FOSTER

1. The sun shines bright in the old Ken-tuck-y home, 'Tis
hunt no more for the 'pos-sum and the coon, On the

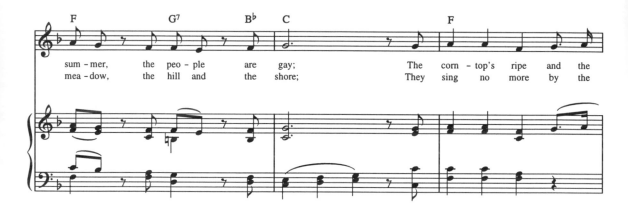

sum - mer, the peo - ple are gay; The corn - top's ripe and the
mea - dow, the hill and the shore; They sing no more by the

mea - dow's in the bloom, While the birds make mus - ic all the day; The
glim - mer of the moon, On the bench by the old___ cab - in door; The

young folks roll on the lit-tle cab-in floor, All mer-ry, all hap-py and bright; By'n
day goes by like a sha-dow o'er the heart, with sor-row where all was de-light; The

bye hard times come a-knock-ing at the door, } Then my old Ken-tuck-y home, Good-night.
time has come when the peo-ple have to part,

CHORUS

Weep no more, my la-dy, O weep no more to-day! We will

sing one song for the old Ken-tuck-y home, For the old Ken-tuck-y home far a-way.

John Brown's Body

March Song of the American War

3. He's gone to be a soldier in the army of the Lord,
   His soul is marching on.

4. John Brown's knapsack is strapp'd upon his back,
   His soul is marching on.

5. His pet lambs will meet him on the way,
   And they'll go marching on.

6. We'll hang Jeff Davis on a sour apple tree.
   As we go marching on.

My Bonnie

American Song

3. Last night as I lay on my pillow,
Last night as I lay on my bed,
Last night as I lay on my pillow,
I dreamed that my Bonnie was dead.
Bring back, *etc.*

4. The winds have blown over the ocean,
The winds have blown over the sea,
The winds have blown over the ocean,
And brought back my Bonnie to me.
Bring back, *etc.*

Polly-Wolly-Doodle

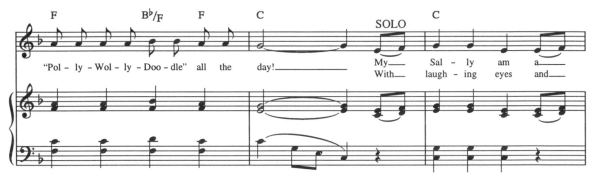

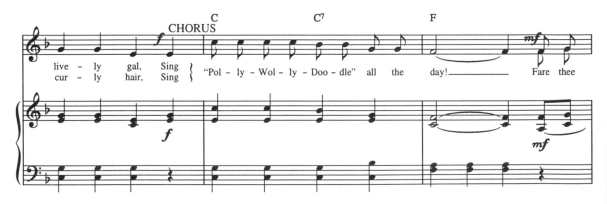

3.
Oh! a grasshopper sittin' on a railroad track,
Sing "Polly-Wolly-Doodle," all the day.
A pickin' his teef wid a carpet tack,
Sing "Polly-Wolly-Doodle," all the day. *(Chorus)*

4.
Behind de barn, down on my knees,
Sing "Polly-Wolly-Doodle," all the day.
I thought I heard a chicken sneeze,
Sing "Polly-Wolly-Doodle," all the day. *(Chorus)*

5.
He sneezed so hard wid de hoopin'-cough,
Sing "Polly-Wolly-Doodle," all the day.
He sneezed his head an' his tail right off,
Sing "Polly-Wolly-Doodle," all the day. *(Chorus)*

The Old Folks At Home

Words & Music by STEPHEN C. FOSTER

Poor Old Joe

Words & Music by STEPHEN C. FOSTER

1. Gone are the days when my heart was young and gay;
2. Why do I weep, when my heart should feel no pain?
3. Where are the hearts, once so hap-py and so free? The

Gone are my friends from the cot-ton fields a-way; Gone from the earth to a
Why do I sigh that my friends come not a-gain? Griev-ing for forms now de-
child-ren so dear, that I held up-on my knee? Gone to the shore where my

bet-ter land I know,
part-ed long a-go, } I hear their gen-tle voic-es call-ing "Poor old Joe!" I'm
soul has long'd to go, (Chorus in

com-ing I'm com-ing for my head is bend-ing low, I hear their gen-tle voic-es call ing "Poor old Joe!"
four parts)

Fine

Swing Low, Sweet Chariot

Swing low, sweet char - i - ot___

Com - ing for to car - ry me home. Swing low, sweet

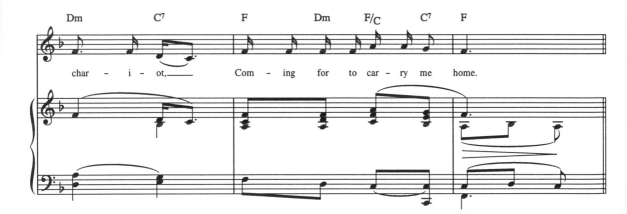

char - i - ot,___ Com - ing for to car - ry me home.

3.
The brightest day that ever I saw,
Coming for to carry me home,
When Jesus washed my sins away,
Coming for to carry me home.
Swing low, *etc.*

4.
I'm sometimes up and sometimes down,
Coming for to carry me home,
But still my soul feels heavenly bound,
Coming for to carry me home.
Swing low, *etc.*

So Early In De Morning

Aloha Oe
(Farewell To Thee)
HAWAIIAN SONG

By H. M. QUEEN LILINOKALANI

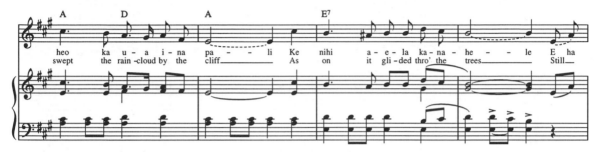

Alouette
(The Lark)

French - Canadian Song

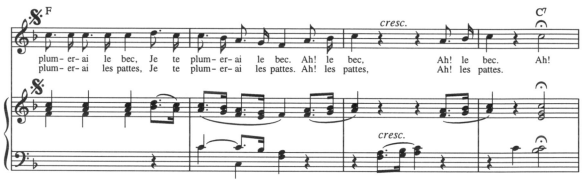

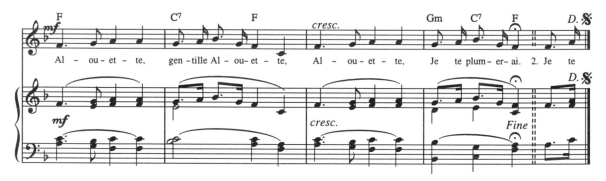

3.
Je te plumerai le dos, *(sing twice)*
Ah! le dos. *etc.*

4.
Je te plumerai la tête, *(sing twice)*
Ah! la tête. *etc.*

5.
Je te plumerai la "falle", *(sing twice)*
Ah! la "falle". *etc.*

6.
Je te plumerai la queue, *(sing twice)*
Ah! la queue. *etc.*

Note: bec (beak).   pattes (legs).   dos (back).   tête (head).   falle (breast).   queue (tail).

A Canadian Boat Song

Words and Music by THOMAS MOORE

1. Faint - ly as tolls the eve - ning chime, Our voic - es keep tune, and our oars keep time, Our voic - es keep tune, and our oars keep time; Soon as the woods on shore look dim, We'll sing at Saint Ann's our part - ing hymn. Row, broth - ers row! the stream runs fast, The Ra - pids are near, and the day - light's past, The Ra - pids are near and the day - light's past.

2. Why should we yet our sail un - furl? There is not a breath the blue wave to curl, There is not a breath the blue wave to curl. But when the wind on blows off the shore, Oh! sweet - ly we'll rest our wea - ry oar. Blow, bree - zes, blow!

Clementine

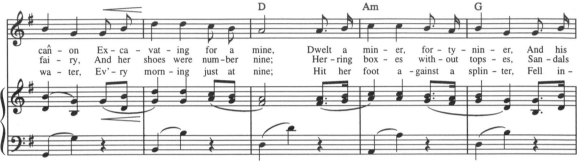

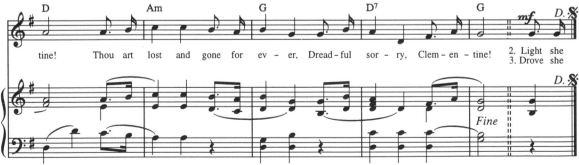

4. Saw her lips above the water
   Blowing bubbles mighty fine;
   But alas! I was no swimmer,
   So I lost my Clementine. *(Chorus)*

5. In a Churchyard near the cañon,
   Where a myrtle doth entwine,
   There grow roses and other posies
   Fertilized by Clementine. *(Chorus)*

6. Then the miner, forty-niner,
   Soon began to peak and pine;
   Thought he "oughter jine" his daughter -
   Now he's with his Clementine. *(Chorus)*

7. In my dreams she still doth haunt me,
   Robed in garments soaked in brine;
   Though in life, I used to hug her,
   Now she's dead, I'll draw the line. *(Chorus)*

Cock Robin

1. Who kill'd Cock Ro - bin? I said the Spar-row, With
2. Who saw him die?__ I said the fly,__ With
3. Who'll toll the bell?__ I said the Bull,__ Be -

my bow and ar - row, I kill'd Cock Ro - bin. All the
my lit - tle eye,__ I saw him die.__
cause I can pull,__ I'll toll the bell.

CHORUS

birds of the air fell a - sigh-ing and a - sob-bing, When they heard of the death of

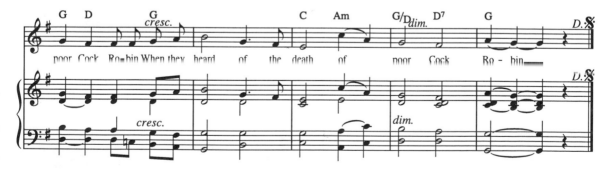

poor Cock Ro-bin When they heard of the death of poor Cock Ro - bin__

D.S.

4. Who'll dig his grave?
   I, said the Owl,
   With my little trowel,
   I'll dig his grave. *(Chorus)*

5. Who'll be the parson?
   I, said the Rook;
   With my little book,
   I'll be the parson. *(Chorus)*

6. Who'll be chief mourner?
   I, said the Dove,
   I mourn for my love,
   I'll be chief mourner. *(Chorus)*

Good Night, ladies!

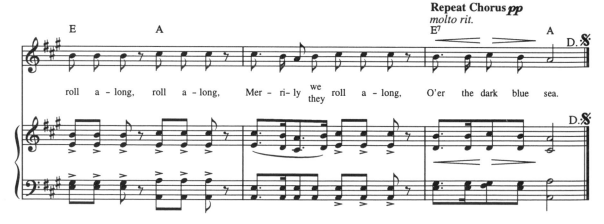

The Keel Row

Allegretto

1. As I cam' doon the
wears a blue
com - ing soon to

Sand - gate, the Sand - gate, the Sand - gate, As I cam' doon the Sand - gate I
bon - net a bon - net, a bon - net, He wears a blue bon - net, A
meet me, to meet me, to meet me, He's com - ing soon to meet me From

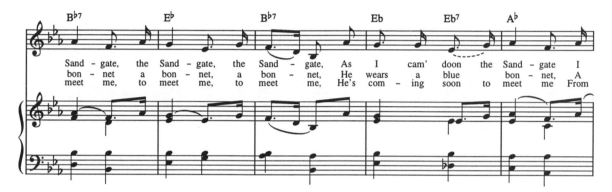

heard a las - sie sing: O mer - ry may the keel row, the keel row, the
dim - ple in his chin.
yon ship in the Tyne

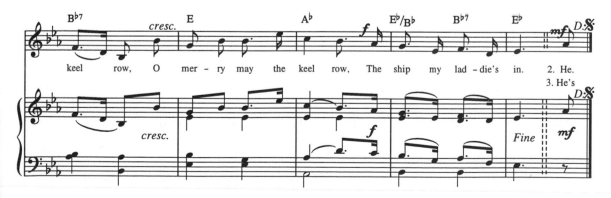

keel row, O mer - ry may the keel row, The ship my lad - die's in. 2. He.
3. He's

The Maple Leaf Forever
(The National Song Of Canada)

Words And Music By ALEXANDER MUIR

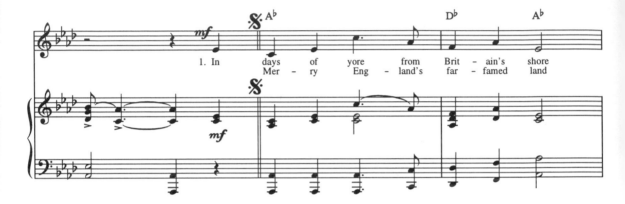

1. In days of yore from Brit – ain's shore
Mer – ry Eng – land's far – famed land

Wolfe the daunt – less he – ro came, And plant – ed firm Bri –
May kind Heav – en sweet – ly smile; God bless Old Scot – land

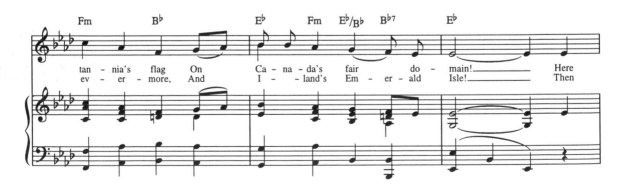

tan – nia's flag On Ca – na – da's fair do – main! Here
ev – er – more, And I – land's Em – er – ald Isle! Then

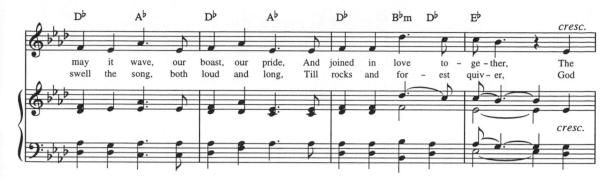

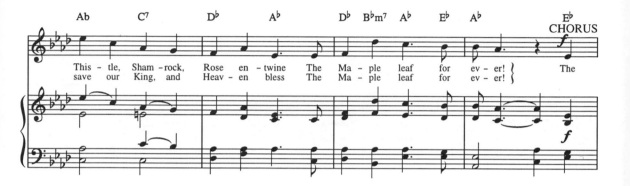

Sweet Genevieve

GEORGE COOPER

HENRY TUCKER

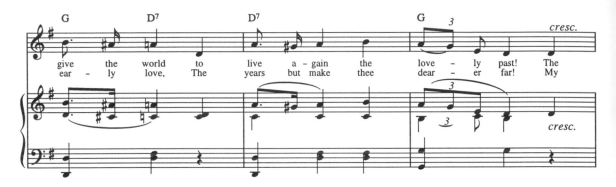

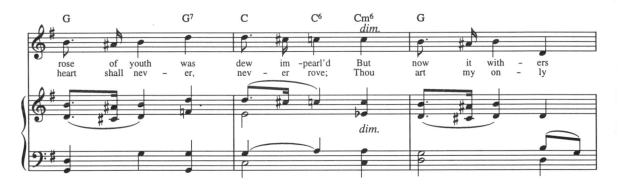

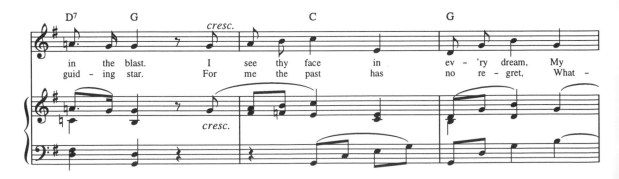

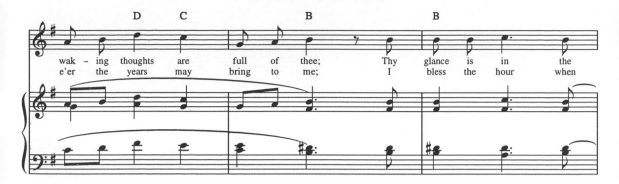

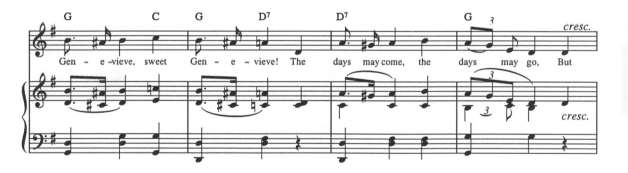

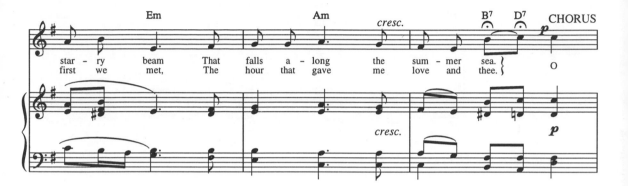

Some Folks Do

S. C. FOSTER

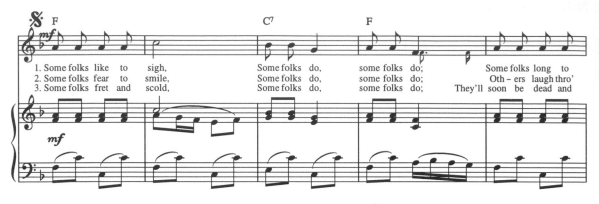

1. Some folks like to sigh, Some folks do, some folks do; Some folks long to
2. Some folks fear to smile, Some folks do, some folks do; Oth- ers laugh thro'
3. Some folks fret and scold, Some folks do, some folks do; They'll soon be dead and

die,
guile, } But that's not me nor you. Long live the mer- ry, mer- ry heart That
cold,

laughs by night and day, Like the Queen of mirth, No mat- ter what some folks say.

4. Some folks get grey hairs,
   Some folks do, some folks do;
   Brooding o'er their cares,
   But that's not me nor you.
   Long live *etc.*

5. Some folks toil and save
   Some folks do, some folks do;
   To buy themselves a grave,
   But that's not me nor you.
   Long live *etc.*

Where Are You Going, My Pretty Maid?

3. What is your father, my pretty maid?
What is your father, my pretty maid?
"My father's a farmer, Sir," she said,
"Sir," she said, "Sir," she said,
"My father's a farmer, Sir," she said.

4. Shall I marry you, my pretty maid?
Shall I marry you, my pretty maid?
"Oh, yes, if you please, kind Sir," she said,
"Sir," she said, "Sir," she said,
"Oh, yes, if you please, kind Sir," she said.

5. And what is your fortune, my pretty maid?
And what is your fortune, my pretty maid?
"My face is my fortune, Sir," she said,
"Sir," she said, "Sir," she said,
"My face is my fortune, Sir," she said.

6. Then I can't marry you, my pretty maid?
Then I can't marry you, my pretty maid?
"Nobody ax'd you, Sir," she said,
"Sir," she said, "Sir," she said,
"Nobody ax'd you, Sir," she said.

Hark, The Bonny Christ Church Bells

DR. ALDRICH

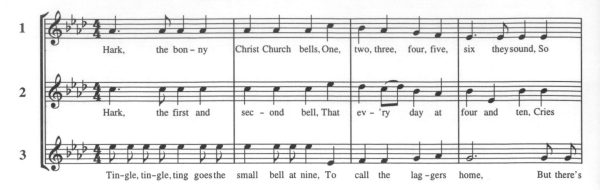

Haste Thee, Nymph

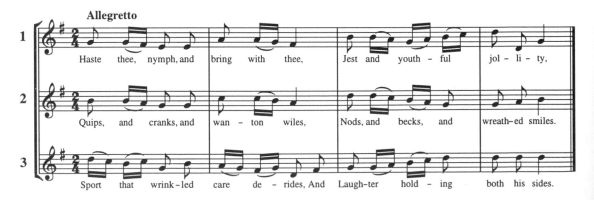

Dame! Get Up And Bake Your Pies

3. Dame! what makes your ducks to die,
Ducks to die, ducks to die;
Dame! what makes your ducks to die,
On Christmas - day in the morning?

4. Their wings are cut and they cannot fly,
Cannot fly, cannot fly;
Their wings are cut and they cannot fly,
On Christmas - day in the morning.

Hickory, Dickory, Dock!

Jack And Jill

Little Bo-Peep

Rock - a - bye Baby

When Good King Arthur Ruled This Land

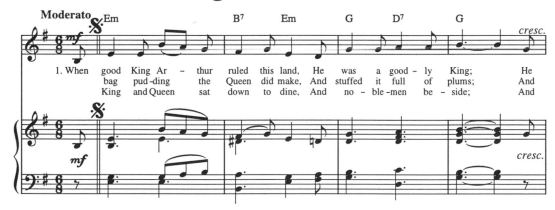

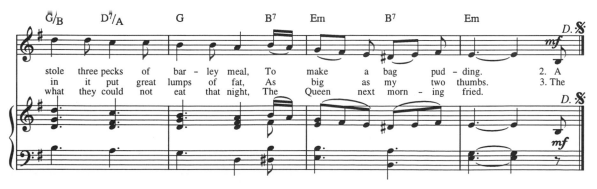

Abide With Me

H. F. LYTE

W. H. MONK

1. A - bide with me! fast falls the e - ven - tide;
2. I need Thy pres - ence ev - 'ry pass - ing hour;
3. I fear no foe, with Thee at hand to bless;

The dark - ness deep - ens, Lord, with me a - bide!
What but Thy grace can foil the tempt - er's pow'r?
Ills have no weight, and tears no bit - ter - ness;

When oth - er help - ers fail, and com - forts flee,
Who like Thy - self my guide and stay can be?
Where is death's sting? Where, grave, thy vic - tor - y?

Help of the help - less, O a - bide with me!
Thro' cloud and sun - shine, O a - bide with me!
I tri - umph still, if Thou a - bide with me!

Glorious Things Of Thee Are Spoken

HAYDN

1. *f* Glo – rious things of thee are spo – ken, Zi – on, ci – ty of our God;
2. *mf* See, the streams of liv – ing wa – ters, Spring – ing from e – ter – nal love,
3. Round each hab – i – ta – tion hov – 'ring, See the cloud and fire ap – pear,
4. *p* Sa – viour, since of Zi – on's ci – ty I, through grace, a mem – ber am.

He Whose word can – not be bro – ken Form'd thee for His own a – bode.
Well sup – ply thy sons and daugh – ters, And all fear of want re – move.
For a glo – ry and a cov – 'ring Show – ing that the Lord is near.
Let the world de – ride or pi – ty, I will glo – ry in Thy Name.

On the Rock of a – ges found – ed, What can shake thy sure re – pose?
Who can faint while such a ri – ver Ev – er flows their thirst to a – suage;
Thus they march, the pil – lar lead – ing, Light by night and shade by day;
Fad – ing is the world's best plea – sure, All it's boast – ed pomp and show;

With sal – va – tion's walls sur – round – ed, Thou mayst smile at all thy foes.
Grace, which like the Lord the Giv – er, Nev – er fails from age to age?
Dai – ly on the man – na feed – ing Which He gives them when they pray.
f Sol – id joys and last – ing trea – sure None but Zi – on's child – ren know. A – men.

Grace
(For These And All Thy Mercies)

From the "Laudi Spirituali"

For these and all Thy mer – cies giv – en, We bless and

praise Thy name, O Lord. May we re – ceive them with thanks – giv – ing,

Ev – er trust – ing in Thy Word: To Thee a – lone be

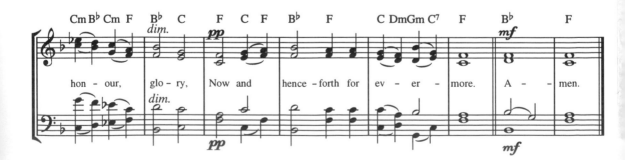

hon – our, glo – ry, Now and hence – forth for ev – er – more. A – men.

Lo! Heaven And Earth

JOACHIM NEANDER (1679)
(Translated by Catherine Winkworth)

D. KORNER (1628)

Paternoster

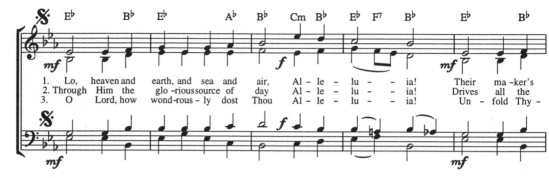

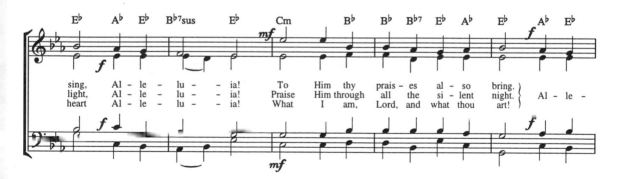

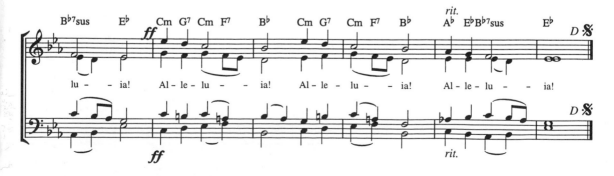

Nearer My God To Thee

SARAH ADAMS

J. B. DYKES

Near - er, my God, to Thee, Near - er__ to Thee, E'en though it be a cross,
Though like the wan - der - er, The sun__ gone down, Dark - ness comes o - ver me,
There let my way ap - pear Steps un - to heaven, All that Thou send - est me
Then, with my wa - king thoughts, Bright with Thy praise, Out of my sto - ny griefs,

That rais - eth me;__ Still all my song shall be,
My rest__ a stone;__ Yet in my dreams I'd be,
In mer - cy given, An - gels to beck - on me,
Be - thel__ I'll raise;__ So by my woes to be

Near - er, my__ God, to Thee, Near - er__ to Thee!

Old Hundredth

REV. W KETHE

Genevan Psalter

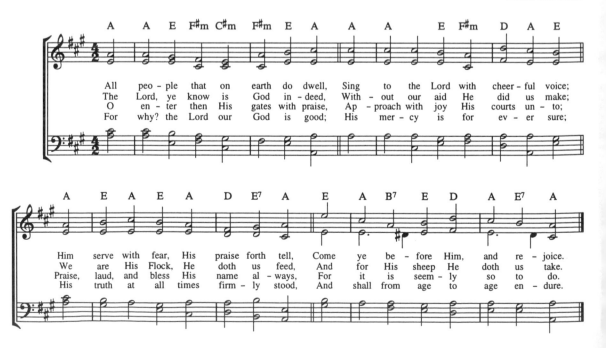

All peo - ple that on earth do dwell, Sing to the Lord with cheer - ful voice;
The Lord, ye know is God in - deed, With - out our aid He did us make;
O en - ter then His gates with praise, Ap - proach with joy His courts un - to;
For why? the Lord our God is good; His mer - cy is for ev - er sure;

Him serve with fear, His praise forth tell, Come ye be - fore Him, and re - joice.
We are His Flock, He doth us feed, And for His sheep He doth us take.
Praise, laud, and bless His name al - ways, For it is seem - ly so to do.
His truth at all times firm - ly stood, And shall from age to age en - dure.

O Come, All Ye faithful

O God, Our Help In Ages Past

Tune - St. Anne

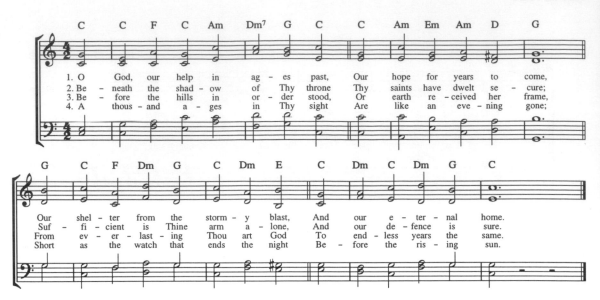

1. O God, our help in ag - es past, Our hope for years to come,
Our shel - ter from the storm - y blast, And our e - ter - nal home.

2. Be - neath the shad - ow of Thy throne Thy saints have dwelt se - cure;
Suf - fi - cient is Thine arm a - lone, And our de - fence is sure.

3. Be - fore the hills in or - der stood, Or earth re - ceived her frame,
From ev - er - last - ing Thou art God To end - less years the same.

4. A thous - and a - ges in Thy sight Are like an eve - ning gone;
Short as the watch that ends the night Be - fore the ris - ing sun.

5. Time, like an ever rolling stream,
Bears all its sons away;
They fly forgotten, as a dream
Dies at the opening day.

6. O God our help in ages past,
Our hope for years to come,
Be thou our guard while troubles last,
And our eternal home!

Glory To Thee, My God

THOMAS KEN

TALLIS

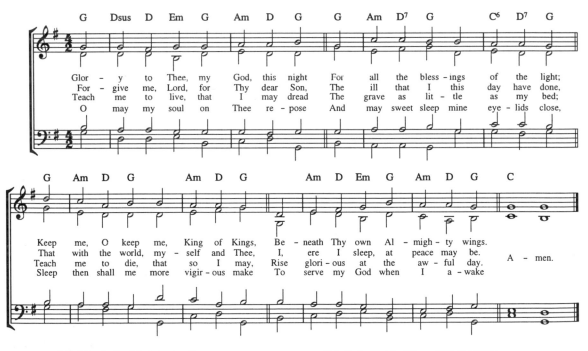

Glor - y to Thee, my God, this night For all the bless - ings of the light;
Keep me, O keep me, King of Kings, Be - neath Thy own Al - migh - ty wings.

For - give me, Lord, for Thy dear Son, The ill that I this day have done,
That with the world, my - self and Thee, I, ere I sleep, at peace may be.

Teach me to live, that I may dread The grave as lit - tle as my bed;
Teach me to die, that so I may, Rise glori - ous at the aw - ful day.

O may my soul on Thee re - pose And may sweet sleep mine eye - lids close,
Sleep then shall me more vigir - ous make To serve my God when I a - wake

A - men.

mf 5. When in the night I sleepless lie,
My soul with heavenly thoughts supply;
Let no ill dreams disturb my rest,
No powers of darkness me molest.

f 6. Praise God for Whom all blessings flow,
Praise Him all creatures here below,
Praise Him above, Angelic host,
Praise FATHER, SON and HOLY GHOST.

Praise, My Soul, The King Of Heaven.

REGENT SQUARE

HENRY SMART.

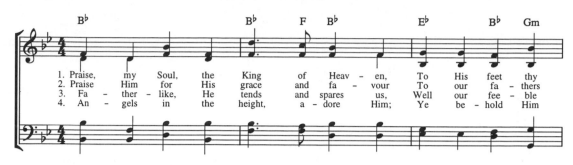

1. Praise, my Soul, the King of Heav - en, To His feet thy
2. Praise Him for His grace and fa - vour To our fa - thers
3. Fa - ther - like, He tends and spares us, Well our fee - ble
4. An - gels in the height, a - dore Him; Ye be - hold Him

tri - bute bring; Ran - somed, healed, re - stored, for - giv - en,
in dis - tress; Praise Him still the same as ev - er,
frame He knows; In His hands He gent - ly bears us,
face to face; Saints tri - umph - ant, bow be - fore Him,

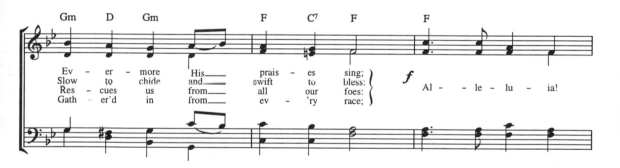

Ev - er - more His____ prais - es sing; }
Slow to chide and____ swift to bless: } *f* Al - - le - lu - ia!
Res - cues us from____ all our foes: }
Gath - er'd in from____ ev - 'ry race; }

Al - le - lu - ia   Praise the ev - er - last - ing King!
                        Glo - rious in His faith - ful - ness.
                        Wide - ly yet His mer - cy flows.
                        Praise with us the God of grace.

Vesper Hymn

THOMAS MOORE

Russian Air

1. Hark the Ves - per hymn is steal - ing O'er the wa - ters
2. Now the moon - light waves re - treat - ing, To the shore it
3. Once a - gain sweet voi - ces ring - ing, Lou - der still the

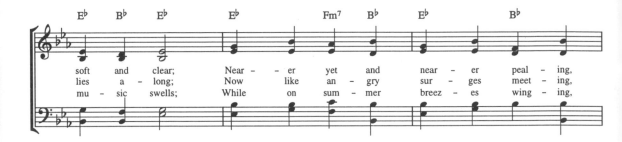

soft and clear; Near - - er yet and near - er peal - ing,
lies a - long; Now like an - gry sur - ges meet - ing,
mu - sic swells; While on sum - mer breez - es wing - ing,

Soft it breaks up - on the ear. Ju - bi - la - te!
Breaks the min - - gled tide of song. Ju - bi - la - te!
Comes the chime of Ves - per bells. Ju - bi - la - te!

Ju - bi - la - te! Ju - bi - la - te! A - - - men

Reproduced and printed by Halstan & Co. Ltd., Amersham, Bucks., England